STICKER ATLAS
The World

Illustrated by
Garry Fleming

Book 1

The Earth's Landscapes

Mountains

Mountains cover 24 percent of Earth's surface. The tops of many mountains are so high that they are covered with ice or snow.

Mountains can be created by volcanoes erupting. When molten rock pours up out of the ground it cools to form many of the mountain formations we see today.

Most of Earth's mountains were formed by great earth movements millions of years ago. They are constantly being worn away to form hills, sand on the beaches or soil on the ground.

The highest mountain on Earth is Mount Everest, in Nepal. It is 8848 metres above sea level. That is as high as 23 Empire State Buildings piled on top of each other!

The longest river in the world is the Nile, which runs from Tanzania, in the centre of Africa, to Egypt in the north, and into the Mediterranean Sea. It is 6670 kilometres long.

Volcanoes

Volcanoes are mountains that have an opening in the top, but with lava and gases trapped underneath. When the lava and gases rumble up from below the ground and escape out of the hole at the top of the volcano, it is called an eruption.

There are many active volcanoes around the world, including Mount St Helens in the USA and Mount Etna in Italy. There are also many extinct volcanoes. This means they no longer erupt.

In Italy around 2000 years ago, Mount Vesuvius erupted burying the entire city of Pompeii under rock and ash.

Rivers

Rivers are large, long trenches that carry fresh water from higher ground to lower ground. Rivers are created when large amounts of water continually travel along the same path, cutting deeper and deeper into the ground until a trench is formed.

The water from rivers can come from under the ground, from rain or from melting ice caps on mountains. Most rivers empty into oceans or lakes, but in some very hot, dry areas, the water can just evaporate before it has a chance to make it out to sea.

Oceans

Oceans are enormous bodies of salt water that surround Earth's continents. Oceans cover about 71 per cent of Earth's surface. There are five oceans: the Pacific, Atlantic, Indian, Southern and Arctic.

Oceans are not only very large, but are also very deep. Out in the middle of the ocean, the bottom is so far down that no light reaches there. Many strange creatures live in this part of the ocean, many of which, it is believed, have not been discovered yet as the water is too deep for humans to explore. The Mariana Trench in the Pacific Ocean has its ocean floor more than 10 kilometres below the surface!

The world's largest ocean is the Pacific, which covers about one third of the Earth's surface.

Lakes

Lakes are large bodies of water surrounded by land. They do not join to the sea like most rivers do.

Lakes are very important to humans and animals alike. Lakes supply many towns and cities with fresh drinking water. Lakes also support a huge amount of plant and animal life, including ducks, frogs and fish.

Over 60 per cent of the world's lakes are in Canada.

Deserts

Deserts are large, dry areas of land that lose more moisture than they gain from rain. Deserts cover about one third of all of the land on Earth.

While deserts are very hot during the day, most deserts get very cold during the night. This is because the air is so dry that it cannot block out the sun's heat during the day, or hold on to the warmth in the air at night.

Deserts are usually great areas of sand or rock with very little plant life.

The whole of Australia could fit inside the Sahara desert in Africa!

Environmental Issues

Air pollution

Air pollution occurs when gases and chemicals created by humans are released into the atmosphere. Some of these chemicals then eat away at the ozone layer, which is the part of Earth's atmosphere that protects us from harsh rays of the sun.

The only way to stop air pollution is for governments, businesses and people at home to try really hard to reduce the amount of pollutants released into the air.

Water pollution

Water pollution occurs when people dump their waste into the sea. Water pollution has a terrible effect on sea life, as it can make their home too dirty to live in. Water pollution also kills coral reefs, which are the sea's natural gardens.

Global warming

The world's average temperature has increased very slightly over the last 100 years. This is known as global warming. Many scientists believe that humans have had such a bad impact on the planet that it is actually us making the world get warmer.

Even a slight change in temperature can have a big impact on our planet. It can cause drought, melt ice caps on mountains and raise sea levels, all of which can affect humans, plant-life and animals.

Resource depletion

When people from a certain country or region of the world use more natural resources than they can replace, it is known as resource depletion. Some of the main causes of resource depletion are mining, fishing, deforestation and drilling and digging for fossil fuels, such as oil and coal.

Resource depletion can have a bad effect on the environment because, as the resources become scarce, people have to go to greater lengths to extract the resources they need from the land.

Overpopulation

Everybody needs resources such as food, drinking water and materials to make shelter, in order to survive. Overpopulation is what happens when there are not enough resources in a certain area to support the number of people living there.

Soil erosion

Erosion is what occurs when the nutrient-rich top layer of the land's soil is washed away by water or carried away in the wind. When this happens, it can make the soil unsuitable for growing crops. The major causes of soil erosion are deforestation, overfarming and overgrazing.

The Continents

Africa

Africa is the world's second largest continent. It is made up of many different nations that each have their own unique and colourful culture. Some of the main languages spoken in Africa are Swahili, Arabic and English.

Africa is considered by many scientists to be the oldest inhabited continent on Earth, which means people lived there before they lived anywhere else.

Africa's landscape is made up of tropical jungle and grassy plains in the south and hot, dry deserts in the north. In fact, Africa is home to the world's largest and hottest desert, the Sahara.

Population: 1 200 000 000
Largest country: Algeria
Longest river: The Nile
Highest mountain: Mount Kilimanjaro
in Tanzania

Africa

Antarctica

Antarctica is a gigantic frozen continent which covers the very bottom part of the earth. There are no native people in Antarctica – the only people who live there are researchers who visit from many different countries around the world. Antarctica has been divided up into a number of different 'claims' (areas that are looked after by a certain country). The largest portion has been claimed by Australia.

Antarctica is the coldest and windiest place on Earth. Even though 98 per cent of Antarctica is covered in ice, and around 70 per cent of all the fresh water on Earth is held in that ice, it is also the world's driest continent. It hardly ever rains in Antarctica!

Population: 1000 to 4000 (but none permanent)
Largest territory: Australian Antarctic Territory
Longest river: The Onyx
Highest mountain: Mount Vinson Massif

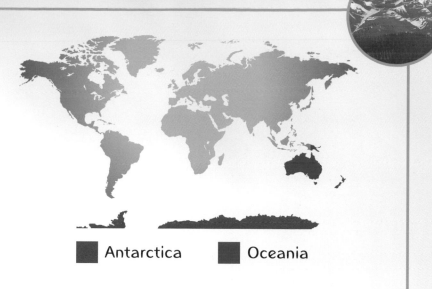

■ Antarctica   ■ Oceania

Oceania

Oceania is the world's smallest and least populated continent. It is made up of Australia, the world's largest island, as well as a number of other island countries including New Zealand and New Guinea. This continent is also sometimes called Australasia.

The first people were thought to have arrived in Australia from southern Asia around 50 000 years ago, and a few thousand years later, some travelled to New Zealand and other Australasian islands.

Around one third of Australia is made up of hot, dry deserts, while New Zealand is very mountainous, and the surrounding islands, including New Guinea, are covered with thick, tropical jungle.

Population: 39 000 000
Largest country: Australia
Longest river: The Murray-Darling
Highest mountain: Mount Wilhelm in Papua New Guinea

Asia

Asia is the world's largest continent. It is also the continent with the most people living on it – in fact, six out of every ten people in the world live in Asia!

Asia is home to the Chinese and Japanese civilisations – some of the oldest in the world. Some interesting inventions that originated in Asia are paper, the compass and kites.

The top part of Asia, made up mostly of Russia, is cold and icy. The bottom part is made up of dense jungle and rainforest, while the central and western areas contain large deserts.

Population: 4 400 000 000
Largest country: China
Longest river: The Yangtze
Highest mountain: Mount Everest in Nepal

Asia

The Great Wall of China is around 6700 kilometres long – that's one and a half times the width of Australia!

The Himalaya Range of Asia is the world's largest mountain system. The Himalayas include eight out of the ten highest peaks in the world.

Europe

Europe is the world's second smallest continent. It is home to many of the world's most famous cities, including London, Paris, Rome and Berlin.

Some of history's most famous civilisations began in Europe, such as the Ancient Greeks and the Roman Empire. Europe has also produced many famous artists, such as Vincent Van Gough, Pablo Picasso and Leonardo da Vinci.

Europe contains the world's largest country, Russia. This country is so big that it actually sits across two continents, Europe and Asia.

Europe

Population: 738 000 000
Largest country: Russia (also partly in Asia)
Longest river: The Volga
Highest mountain: Mount Elbrus in Russia

Europe is also home to the world's smallest country, the Vatican City. A small territory within the borders of Italy, the Vatican City is the home of the leader of the Catholic church, the Pope.

The climate in the north of Europe is cold and icy, while in the south it is sunny and warm.

North America

North America is made up of three very large countries: the United States of America (USA), Canada and Mexico, as well as Greenland and many other smaller nations and islands.

During the last ice ages, North America used to be connected to Asia by a land bridge that ran from the US state of Alaska to the eastern part of Russia.

The northern parts of the continent are freezing – in parts of Canada the temperature can be as low as minus 40 degrees Celsius. The southern region, including Texas and Mexico, is hot and dry, and much of it is made up of desert.

North America

Population: 528 000 000
Largest country: Canada
Longest river: The Mississippi–Missouri
Highest mountain: Mount McKinley in the USA

South America

South America is the world's fourth largest continent. Over half of the people in South America live in Brazil, its largest country.

Most of the people of South America speak Spanish or Portuguese, but many also speak the traditional languages that existed before European settlement.

South America is home to many amazing natural features, such as the world's highest waterfall, largest river, driest desert, longest mountain range and largest rainforest.

The Amazon rainforest, the world's largest, is home to more plant and animal species than anywhere else on Earth.

■ South America

Population: 387 000 000
Largest country: Brazil
Longest river: The Amazon
Highest mountain: Mount Aconcagua in Argentina

How to use your giant wall map

The wall map shows each of the world's six inhabited continents. Not included on the map is the seventh continent, Antarctica. This is because whilst groups of people, such as research scientists, do visit Antarctica, no population of people live there continually.

Around the edges of the continents are boxes for you to place the flag stickers into. The flag stickers have the names of the countries printed under them. Match the sticker to its corresponding box on the wall map.

North America

Antigua and Barbuda	Barbados	Belize	Canada	Costa Rica	Cuba	Dominica	Dominican Republic	El Salvador	Grenada
Guatemala	Haiti	Honduras	Jamaica	Mexico	Nicaragua	Panama	The Bahamas	Trinidad and Tobago	United States of America

The wall map has lots of little pictures, called icons, on each of the continents. Have a look at the icons. Do you recognise them? The icons can tell you about what kinds of people, animals, places or things can be found in that part of the world.

Antigua and Barbuda	Barbados	Belize	Canada	Costa Rica	Cuba	Dominica	Dominican Republic
El Salvador	Grenada	Guatemala	Haiti	Honduras	Jamaica	Mexico	Nicaragua
Panama	The Bahamas	Trinidad and Tobago	United States of America	Argentina	Bolivia	Brazil	Chile
Colombia	Ecuador	Guyana	Paraguay	Peru	Suriname	Uruguay	Venezuela
Albania	Andorra	Armenia	Austria	Azerbaijan	Belarus	Belgium	Bosnia and Herzegovina
Bulgaria	Croatia	Cyprus	Czech Republic	Denmark	Estonia	Finland	France
Germany	Greece	Hungary	Iceland	Ireland	Italy	Latvia	Lithuania
Malta	Norway	Poland	Portugal	Serbia	Slovakia	Slovenia	Spain
Sweden	Switzerland	The Netherlands	Ukraine	United Kingdom	Vatican City	Algeria	Angola
Benin	Botswana	Burkina Faso	Burundi	Cameroon	Cape Verde	Central African Republic	Chad
Comoros	Congo	Côte d'Ivoire	Democratic Republic of the Congo	Djibouti	Egypt	Equatorial Guinea	Eritrea
Ethiopia	Gabon	Ghana	Guinea	Guinea-Bissau	Kenya	Libya	Madagascar
Malawi	Mali	Mauritania	Morocco	Mozambique	Namibia	Niger	Nigeria
Republic of the Sudan	Senegal	Sierra Leone	Somalia	South Africa	South Sudan	Swaziland	Tanzania

The Gambia	Tunisia	Uganda	Western Sahara	Zambia	Zimbabwe	Afghanistan	Bahrain
Bangladesh	Bhutan	Brunei	Cambodia	India	Indonesia	Iran	Iraq
Israel	Japan	Jordan	Kazakhstan	Laos	Lebanon	Malaysia	Mongolia
Myanmar (Burma)	North Korea	Oman	Pakistan	People's Republic of China	Philippines	Russia	Saudi Arabia
Singapore	South Korea	Sri Lanka	Syria	Tajikistan	Thailand	Turkey	Turkmenistan
United Arab Emirates	Uzbekistan	Vietnam	Yemen	Australia	East Timor	Fiji	Micronesia
New Zealand	Palau	Papua New Guinea	Samoa	Solomon Islands	Tonga	Vanuatu	

STICKER ATLAS
Animals

Illustrated by
Garry Fleming

Book 2

Animal Classes

Animal classes are groups of animals that are all alike in certain ways. Scientists have created these groups to make it easy to identify animals. The animal kingdom is divided into many classes, including mammals, birds, fish, reptiles, amphibians and invertebrates.

Mammals

The best way to tell if an animal is a mammal is to ask, 'does it have hair?' and 'does it feed milk to its young?'. If the answer to both of these questions is 'yes', it's a mammal.

Largest mammal: Blue whale, up to 33 metres in length

Smallest mammal: Bumblebee bat, 30–40 millimetres in length

Now, answer these two questions about the following animals: a human, a cat and a giraffe. Yes, they are all mammals. Some other mammals are dogs, elephants, lions, possums and mice, as well as around 5000 other types of animals.

Mammals can be found in virtually every part of the world. There are mammals that live on land, such as bears, monkeys and possums; mammals that live in the ocean, such as whales and dolphins; and even mammals that fly, such as bats.

Dolphin skin

Elephant skin

Grizzly bear skin

Birds

Birds are the only animals in the world that have feathers. Baby birds hatch out of eggs. A bird's wings and feathers make it able to fly, although some birds, such as ostriches and penguins, cannot fly.

Most birds are omnivorous, which means they eat both meat and vegetation. Some birds, such as sparrows and emus, eat fruit, seeds and small creatures including worms or insects. Some larger birds, such as eagles and vultures, eat other animals including mice, smaller birds or meat they find on animals that have already died.

Birds can be found on every continent on Earth: from emus in the desert plains of Australia, to the penguins in icy Antarctica.

Largest bird: Ostrich, up to 2.7 metres tall

Smallest bird: Bee hummingbird, around 6 centimetres in length

Fish

Fish scales

Fish are animals that live in water. All fish have scales, fins and gills. Gills are tiny slits in the side of their heads that allow fish to breathe oxygen from water. Some of the earliest fish, millions of years ago, did not have scales or jawbones.

There are many different and wonderful types of fish, from colourful reef fish, to sea dragons and sharks. Some fish, such as piranhas and salmon, eat other fish. Some fish, such as whale sharks and manta rays, eat mostly plants.

Fish can be found in most bodies of water on Earth, from lakes and rivers to oceans.

Largest fish: Whale shark, up to 15 metres in length

Smallest fish: Stout infantfish, up to 8 millimetres in length

Reptiles

Reptiles are cold-blooded animals that have scales. Because reptiles are cold-blooded, they rely on the sun to heat their bodies. This is why they can often be seen lying in direct sunlight. When their bodies become too hot, reptiles can lie in the shade or go for a swim to cool off.

There are thousands of different types of reptiles, from snakes and turtles to chameleons. Most reptiles eat meat including insects and small mammals, such as mice and rats, although some reptiles eat only plants.

Reptiles live on every continent except Antarctica. They live in all sorts of habitats, from deserts to rainforests and jungles.

Largest reptile: Saltwater crocodile, up to 7 metres in length

Smallest reptile: Dwarf gecko, around 6 millimetres in length

Amphibians

Amphibians are animals that are born in the water and breathe through gills, but as they grow, they develop lungs and are able to live on land.

There are many different types of amphibians, but some of the most common are frogs, toads and salamanders.

Amphibians can be found in almost every part of the world, except in the Arctic regions.

Frog skin   Snake skin

Largest amphibian: Chinese giant salamander, up to 1.8 metres in length

Smallest amphibian: Brazilian gold frog, around 9.8 millimetres in length

Invertebrates

Invertebrates are animals without backbones. They are by far the largest group of animals: more than 98 per cent of all animals in the world are invertebrates. Possibly the most well-known types of invertebrates are arthropods, which include insects, arachnids, molluscs and crustaceans.

Insects are creatures that have three body sections: a head, a thorax and an abdomen. Insects also have six legs and two antennae. Members of the insect group include ladybirds, beetles and dragonflies. Insects alone make up more than half of the known animal species on Earth.

Arachnids are creatures that don't have wings, have eight legs and two body sections. Members of this group include spiders, scorpions, mites and ticks.

Molluscs are animals that also have three body sections: a head, a middle section containing its organs and a foot to help with movement. Some different types of molluscs are snails, clams and octopuses.

Crustaceans are animals with hard outer shells that have two pairs of antennae. This group includes crabs, prawns and barnacles.

Invertebrates can be found just about everywhere on Earth, from icy-cold climates and hot, dry deserts to the deepest parts of the ocean.

Butterfly wing

Crab shell

Dragonfly wing

Largest invertebrate: Giant squid, up to 18 metres in length

The Continents
Africa

Africa is the world's second largest continent. The northern part of Africa is made up mostly of desert, but the south is made up of fertile farmland, savannah grass plains and even jungles. This means a great many different types of animals call Africa home.

Animals such as ostriches, jackals, camels, foxes and scorpions can be found in the hot, dry north of Africa. Only animals that can survive on very small amounts of water can live in this area.

African elephants are the largest land mammals in the world. They can weigh over 5000 kilograms!

Animals that can be found in the grassy savannahs include giraffes, zebras, meerkats, gazelles and many other large herbivores that are able to travel across the plains eating the grass. In turn, these herbivores attract large predators, such as lions and leopards.

Animals that can be found in African jungles include gorillas, fruit bats, parrots, snakes and many types of insects.

Antarctica

Antarctica is the large frozen continent found at the very bottom of the earth. Antarctica is the only continent that does not have native people, but it does have some wildlife.

Animals that can be found in Antarctica include penguins, terns, a few species of arthropods such as mites and lice, and some marine animals such as whales, seals and sharks.

Antarctica is frozen all year round, and the average temperature is an icy minus 57 degrees Celsius, which makes it too cold for most animals to survive the harsh climate.

During the Antarctic breeding season, blue whales can eat enough food every day to feed a human adult for about four years!

Asia

Asia is the largest continent on Earth. It has a wide variety of landscapes and climates, from the snow and ice-covered mountainous areas in the north, to the lush tropical jungle, white sandy beaches and warm oceans in the south, and deserts in the west. This is why such a large number of different animals can be found in Asia.

In the snowy north, animals such as wolves, musk deer, reindeer and arctic foxes can be found. In the hotter, jungle areas animals such as elephants, orang-utans and many species of insects and lizards dwell. Fierce predators such as tigers and panthers also roam wild. Asia's most famous animal, the giant panda, lives in the central forest areas.

The name 'orang-utan' actually means 'man of the forest' in Malay. Orang-utans live only in small areas of Malaysia and Indonesia.

Oceania

Oceania is made up of many islands in the southern Pacific ocean. Oceania includes Australia, which is made up of warm, tropical regions in the north, deserts in the middle and west, and fertile farmland in the south. Even though it is the world's smallest continent, Australia is home to some of the world's oddest creatures. The wild dingo roams the bushy wilderness, frilled lizards bask in the desert and kookaburras laugh from the trees. Some of the world's most venomous snakes can be found throughout the continent, including the inland taipan and the tiger snake.

Perhaps Australia's most interesting animals are the marsupials. Marsupials are mammals that give birth to live babies at a very early stage of their development, and then the baby crawls up the mother's stomach and into her pouch where it begins to feed on milk. Some Australian marsupials are kangaroos, koalas and wombats.

Australian platypuses can eat their own bodyweight in food in any 24-hour period.

Europe

Europe is the world's second smallest continent. The north of Europe is made up of cold, icy regions, while the south has a warm, mild climate. Much of Europe is covered in farmland where pigs and cows are some of the most popular animals farmed.

Small mammals, such as moles and badgers, can be found throughout most of Europe. Large, predatory mammals, such as the grey wolf, are not so common, and can be found only in parts of western and northern Europe. This is because humans are now living on much of the land where these animals used to roam.

Europe is also home to many types of birds, including swans, ducks and quails.

North America

Like most of the continents, North America has many different types of landscapes and climates, which are home to many different types of animals.

At the top of North America, powerful grizzly bears can be found fishing for salmon from lakes and streams, while bald eagles soar high above the desert plains in the central regions.

Mountain goats and cougars roam the Rocky Mountains, and beavers build dams in the streams of forest areas.

Fossil remains show that millions of years ago, North America was probably home to the greatest number of dinosaurs in the world!

hedgehog sheds its baby spines for adult spines. his is called 'quilling'.

South America

South America is a continent that has many wonderful and interesting animals. Much of the top half of the continent is made up of the gigantic Amazon Rainforest, which is home to thousands of animal species. Some of the most well-known animals that dwell in the Amazon are the sloths that live high up in the trees, giant anacondas and boa constrictors, brightly coloured macaws and big tarantula spiders.

The Andes Mountains are an enormous mountain range that runs along the western part of South America. Animals such as llamas, condors and pumas call these rocky regions 'home'.

The Galapagos Islands, which are located off the western tip of South America, are renowned for being home to many animals that do not live in the wild anywhere else on Earth. The most famous of these are the giant Galapagos tortoises.

Other animals that can be found in South America include armadillos, toucans, flamingos and capybaras. The legendary vampire bat is also a resident of South America.

Scientists believe that wild Galapagos tortoises can live for up to 200 years!

Exciting Animal Facts

Chimpanzees are the most closely related animals to humans. In fact, many scientists believe that we share around 98% of our DNA!

Polar bears are the largest land predators in the world. The largest ever recorded polar bear weighed around 1000 kilograms!

Scarab beetles were considered sacred in ancient Egyptian times.

Chameleons can change their skin to a variety of different colours! The change in colour depends on the temperature, the amount of light present and even their mood.

Capybaras are the world's largest rodents.

Giant pandas are highly endangered. It is believed that there are only about 1500 to 2000 still living in the wild.

Scientists do not know for certain why flamingos sometimes stand on only one leg.

Platypuses and echidnas are the only mammals in the world that lay eggs instead of giving birth to live young.

How to use your giant wall map

The wall map shows each of the world's six inhabited continents. Each continent is placed inside a box so that you can clearly see what countries are part of that continent.

On and around the continents are spaces for you to place the stickers of animals that live on that continent. The stickers have the names of the animals printed under them. Choose an animal sticker, then look for a picture that matches that sticker on the map. Place the sticker over the picture, and you're done!

North America

Arctic Ocean

ALASKA (USA)

GREENLAND

Hudson Bay

CANADA

UNITED STATES OF AMERICA

Gulf of Mexico

BAHAMAS

CUBA

DOMINICAN REPUBLIC

HAITI

PUERTO RICO

HAWAII (USA)

BELIZE

JAMAICA

Pacific Ocean

GUATEMALA   HONDURAS

TRINIDAD & TOBAGO

EL SALVADOR   NICARAGUA

COSTA RICA

PANAMA

MEXICO

Many animals live on more than one continent. For instance, wolves live in North America and Europe and badgers live in Africa, Europe and Asia. What other animals can you think of that might live on more than one continent?

Camel
Jackal
Crocodile
Hyena
Leopard
Ostrich
Lio
Vulture
Scarab beetle
Hippopotamus
Rhinoceros
Giraffe
Chimpanzee
Zebra
Meerkat
Gorilla
Butterfly
Fruit bat
Manc
Lemur
Flamingo
Armadillo
Toucan
Macaw
Galapagos tortoise
Sloth
Piranha
Aardvark
Tarantula
Boa constrictor
Capybara
Guinea pig
Red kangaroo
Platypus
Bullfrog
Kiwi
Dingo
Chameleon
Tasn
Bird of paradise
Sheep
Koala
Cockatoo
Frilled lizard
Ring-tailed possum
Tiger snake
Echidna
Quokka
Kookaburra
Weasel
Wombat
Dragonfly
Chicken
Panda
Elephant (Asian)
Mongoose
Giant flying squirrel
Black panther
Orang-utan
Tiger
Peacock
Yak
Atlantic puffin
Ladybird
Badger
Komodo dragon
Donkey
Hermit crab
Reindeer
Arctic fox
Wolf
Cow
S
Fire salamander
Toad
Rat
Common crane
Squirrel
Mole
Duck

Polar bear

Coyote

Raccoon

Green tree frog

Atlantic salmon

Bobcat

Gila monster

Grizzly bear

Snowy owl

Eagle

Turkey

Opossum

Arctic hare

Mountain goat

Skunk

Seal

Beaver

Chipmunk

Penguin

Blue whale

Albatross

Killer whale

Dugong

Narwhal

Angelfish

Sea star

Great white shark

Pufferfish

Hammerhead shark

Whale shark

Manta ray

Clownfish

Sea turtle

Walrus

Pelican

Jellyfish

Dolphin

Sea dragon

Octopus

Sea otter

STICKER ATLAS
Space

Book 3

The universe

The word 'universe' refers to everything in all of space and time. The universe is made up of everything that exists. This includes planets, stars and galaxies. Many scientists believe the big bang theory, which states that the universe was created about 13.73 billion years ago due to an explosion called the 'big bang'. Before that, everything in the universe was contained in a hot and dense state called the 'Planck Epoch'. After the big bang, the universe began to expand, and it is still doing so.

Gravity is when objects of smaller mass are pulled towards objects of larger mass.

The Milky Way is about 100 000 light years in diameter.

Milky Way galaxy

The Milky Way

The Milky Way is the name of the galaxy in which our solar system is located. The Milky Way is spiral shaped.

Groups of stars cluster together to form galaxies, and galaxies cluster together to form superclusters.

Stars and galaxies

The universe is full of stars. Stars are massive balls of plasma (a kind of hot gas) that are held together by gravity. Planets are objects that orbit (complete a full circle of) a star. The closest star to Earth is the sun, which the earth orbits, along with the other planets in our solar system. The solar system belongs to the Milky Way galaxy, which is a member of a supercluster of galaxies we call the Local Group.

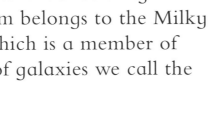

A supercluster of galaxies

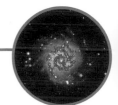

The sun

The sun is one of billions of stars in the Milky Way galaxy and is made of hydrogen and helium gas. Hydrogen gets turned to helium within the sun, producing energy.

The sun is located about 149 600 000 km (92 957 130 mi) from Earth. It supports life on Earth, controlling the climate and weather.

The core of the sun is extremely hot, about 15 000 000°C (27 000 000°F); its surface (called the 'photosphere') is about 5500°C (9930°F). The sun's corona or outer atmosphere can be seen during total solar eclipses.

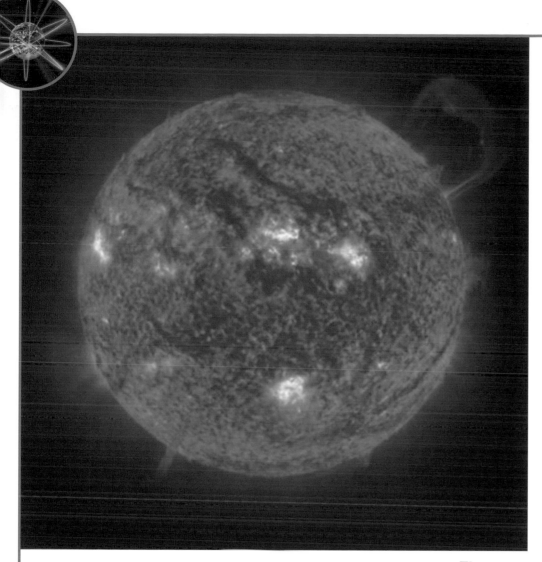

The sun

Even though it is about 1 400 000 times the size of Earth, the sun is a below-average size for a star.

Solar eclipse

A solar eclipse occurs when the moon passes directly between the sun and Earth. A partial eclipse is when the moon covers only part of the sun. A total eclipse is when the moon covers the sun completely, blocking out its light.

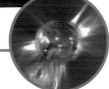

Total solar eclipse

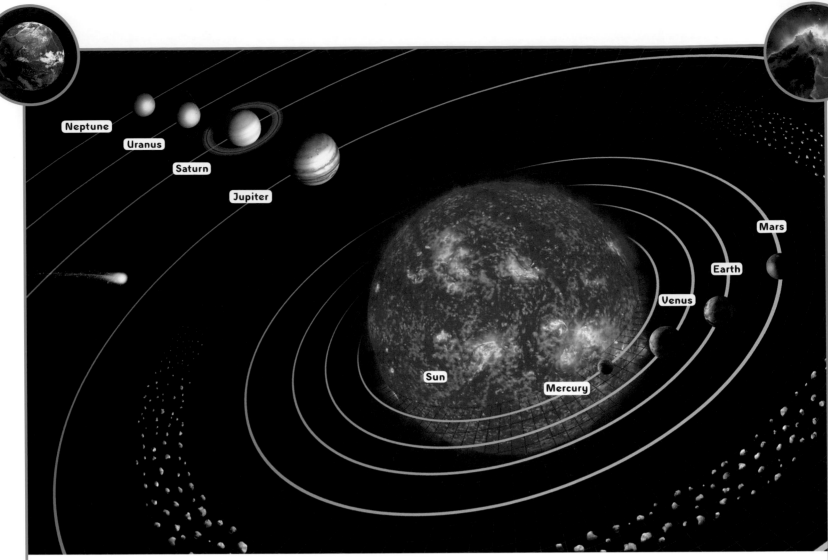

Neptune
Uranus
Saturn
Jupiter
Mars
Earth
Venus
Sun
Mercury

The solar system

A solar system consists of a star (or sometimes two or more stars!) and the objects that orbit it.

Our solar system is thought to have formed about 4.6 billion years ago when a giant molecular cloud collapsed. The centre of the cloud became hot and dense, eventually becoming the sun, our star. Particles of dust then clumped together to form massive boulders, becoming the planets as they are today.

Because the sun is so massive in comparison to the planets, they are drawn into its gravity, which is why the planets are continually orbiting the sun.

There are four smaller planets close to the sun – Mercury, Venus, Earth and Mars. They are mainly made of rock and metal and are called 'terrestrial planets'. An asteroid belt divides the terrestrial planets from the 'gas giants': Jupiter, Saturn, Uranus and Neptune. These planets are massive and made mostly of gases like hydrogen and helium. After the gas giants is the Kuiper Belt.

The planets orbit the sun in an anti-clockwise direction, and their orbits are 'elliptical' (oval-shaped).

Mercury

Mercury is the closest planet to the sun. From Earth, Mercury can be seen best in the morning or at twilight.

Mercury has many craters made by meteorites crashing into its surface billions of years ago. The temperature of Mercury ranges from around −180°C to 427°C (−292°F to 800°F). Mercury has a large core made of iron, almost no atmosphere, and no moons.

Mercury

Venus

Venus

Venus is the second-closest planet to the sun. Viewed from Earth at night, Venus is the brightest object after the moon.

Venus is covered in clouds of sulfuric acid and its atmosphere consists mainly of carbon dioxide. Venus is dusty and dry, and it has constant, extremely hot temperatures (about 860°F [460°C], which are a result of the dense carbon atmosphere trapping infrared radiation from the sun. Venus is covered in volcanoes, some of them reaching 100 km (62 mi) across. It has no moons.

When Soviet scientists sent space probes to Venus, they detected constant lightning and thunder. As there is no rain on Venus, this lightning may have been formed by ash from giant volcanic eruptions.

Earth

Earth is the third planet from the sun, and the only planet in the solar system that we're sure has liquid water on its surface. This is what enables life to exist on Earth. As far as we know, Earth is the only place in the universe that supports life. The earth's magnetic field and layer of ozone serve to protect life on the surface from harmful radiation and from meteorite bombardment. It takes the earth 365.25 days to orbit the sun.

Earth's core is made mainly of iron. The surface, called the 'crust', is a rocky shell that is divided into large plates.

Earth's magnetic field stretches into space and protects the earth from solar wind – high energy particles that come from the sun.

The United States sent a spaceship to the moon in 1969. Neil Armstrong and Buzz Aldrin were the astronauts who walked on the moon and spent a day on its surface.

The moon

When a planet has a natural satellite (an object that orbits it) we call this a 'moon'. Earth has one moon. The moon makes an orbit around the earth every 27.3 days. There is no air or liquid on the moon's rocky surface. It is marked with many craters left from asteroid collisions.

The reason that the moon seems to change shape from night to night is that its exposure to the sun alters.

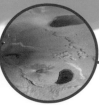

Mars

Mars is the fourth planet from the sun. It is sometimes called the 'Red Planet' because of its colour, which is due to the iron oxide of its surface. Mars has a thin atmosphere and probably a small iron core.

Mars is home to Olympus Mons, the highest known mountain in our solar system, as well as Valles Marineris, the largest canyon. Water ice has been found on Mars, and it is possible that Mars used to have a lot of water on its surface and perhaps life. Mars has two small irregular-shaped moons, Phobos and Deimos.

Mars's moons are probably asteroids that have been captured by its gravity.

Mars

Deimos

Phobos

Asteroid belt

If a large asteroid collided with the earth's surface, it could cause devastation and temperature change. A large asteroid crashing into the earth may have been the reason that dinosaurs became extinct.

Asteroid belt

Between Mars and Jupiter is the asteroid belt. This region of the solar system is full of objects called asteroids. The asteroid belt is also home to Ceres, a large asteroid that has been classified as a dwarf planet. Asteroids were probably formed from fragments of planets that have broken off. When asteroids collide, they make smaller fragments of rock called meteoroids. These sometimes crash into Earth as meteorites.

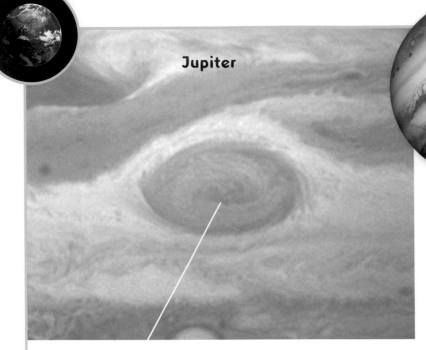

Jupiter

The Great Red Spot

Jupiter

Jupiter

Jupiter is the fifth planet from the sun and the largest planet in the solar system. It is a gas giant, and its colourful-looking surface is caused by clouds in its atmosphere made of ammonia, methane and water ice.

Jupiter is mainly made of hydrogen and helium, probably with a small rocky core. The planet is surrounded by faint planetary rings made of dust.

Jupiter has at least 67 moons, including the Galilean moons that were discovered in 1610 by Galileo Galilei.

Io

Callisto

Ganymede

Europa

The Great Red Spot is a giant storm on Jupiter that has been going for over 300 years. It is larger than two Earths.

Saturn's rings

Saturn

Saturn

Saturn is the sixth planet from the sun and the second-largest planet. This gas giant is composed mainly of hydrogen, with a small core of

rock and ice. Saturn is known for its rings, which are made mainly of ice particles. There are seven major rings and thousands of smaller ringlets.

Saturn has 62 known moons, including Titan, the solar system's second-largest moon after Jupiter's Ganymede.

Saturn's orbit around the sun takes about 29.5 years.

Uranus

Uranus

Uranus is the seventh planet from the sun. Unlike Jupiter and Saturn, Uranus and Neptune fit into the category of 'ice giants', as they contain larger amounts of ices. Uranus's atmosphere is made mainly of water, ammonia and methane, making it the coldest planet in the solar system. Its surface has almost no features apart from some fast-moving clouds.

Uranus is tilted, and orbits the sun nearly on its side.

Neptune

Neptune

Neptune is the eighth planet from the sun. It has 14 moons, including Triton, its largest. Neptune is an ice giant made mainly of hydrogen and helium, with an icy, rocky core. The planet's blue appearance is due to the traces of methane in its outer regions. Although Neptune's surface is featureless, it has visible weather patterns and storms.

Neptune on Triton's horizon

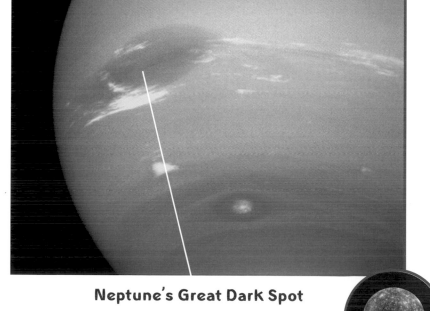

Neptune's Great Dark Spot

Pluto and the Kuiper Belt

Beyond Neptune lies the Kuiper Belt, containing Pluto, the second-largest known dwarf planet in the solar system (after Eris). Pluto used to be classified as a planet, but was reclassified as a dwarf planet in 2006. Pluto's core is most probably rocky with a thin atmosphere of nitrogen and methane. It has five known moons. The largest is Charon.

Unlike the rocky asteroid belt, the Kuiper Belt objects are mainly made of ice. As well as Pluto, the dwarf planets Haumea and Makemake can be found in the Kuiper Belt.

The New Horizons spacecraft was launched in 2006. It passed Pluto and its moons in 2015 and sent images and data back to Earth.

Halley's comet is the most famous comet, as it is easily visible to the naked eye and can be seen from Earth every 75 to 76 years. Halley's comet will next appear in mid-2061.

Comets

Comets are small objects that orbit the sun. When a comet gets close to the sun, the solar radiation affects the comet's nucleus and makes it form a cloud of dust and gas called a 'coma'. This cloud is blown by the solar wind into an enormous tail. The coma and the tail are illuminated by the sun, and can become visible from Earth when the comet passes through the inner solar system.

Halley's comet

NASA's twin Exploration Rovers landed on the surface of Mars in 2004. They have been very helpful in providing information about the surface of the 'Red Planet'.

Space exploration

Space exploration involves using technology and astronomy to explore outer space. From Earth, we can see the moon, planets, distant stars and even other galaxies. Telescopes are very useful tools for observing outer space from Earth.

Although people have always been able to observe the sky, humans and robots have only been able to physically explore space since the early 20th century. In 1957, Sputnik 1 was the first man-made object to orbit Earth. The first moon landing took place in 1969. Since then, many manned and unmanned spacecraft have explored space.

The Hubble Space Telescope was launched into orbit by NASA (the USA's National Aeronautics and Space Administration) in 1990 and is an extremely useful tool for observing space.

The International Space Station is a research laboratory being assembled in Low Earth Orbit. It is a joint program of the United States, Russia, Japan, Canada and ten European nations.

How to use your giant wall chart

The wall chart shows our solar system and the objects that inhabit it, as well as some features of space exploration. On and around the wall chart is space for you to place the stickers that complete these images.

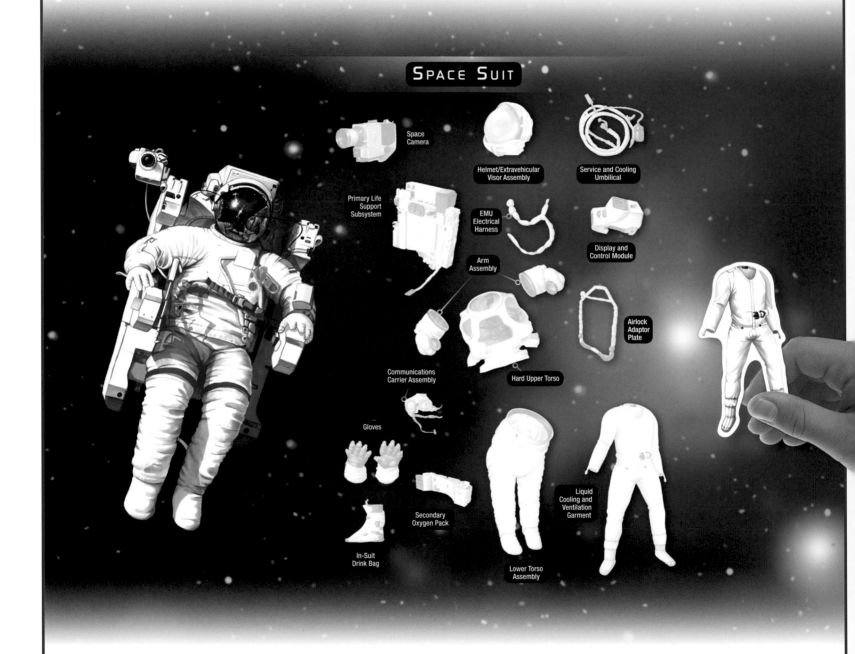

SPACE SUIT

Space Camera

Helmet/Extravehicular Visor Assembly

Service and Cooling Umbilical

Primary Life Support Subsystem

EMU Electrical Harness

Display and Control Module

Arm Assembly

Airlock Adaptor Plate

Communications Carrier Assembly

Hard Upper Torso

Gloves

Secondary Oxygen Pack

Liquid Cooling and Ventilation Garment

In-Suit Drink Bag

Lower Torso Assembly

The stickers have labels printed under them. Choose a sticker, then look for a picture that matches that sticker on the chart. Place the sticker over the picture and you're done!

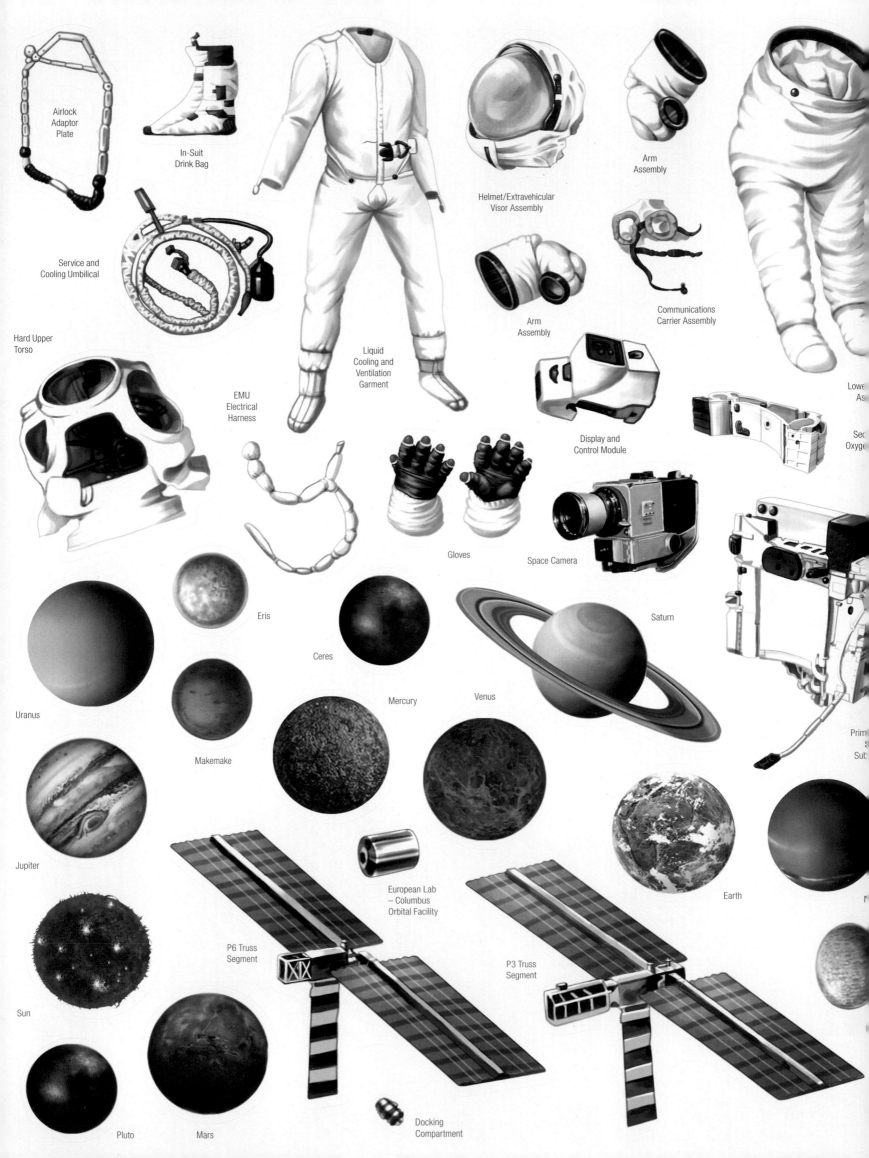

Airlock Adaptor Plate

In-Suit Drink Bag

Helmet/Extravehicular Visor Assembly

Arm Assembly

Service and Cooling Umbilical

Arm Assembly

Communications Carrier Assembly

Hard Upper Torso

EMU Electrical Harness

Liquid Cooling and Ventilation Garment

Display and Control Module

Low___ As___

Sec___ Oxyge___

Gloves

Space Camera

Eris

Ceres

Mercury

Venus

Saturn

Prim___ S___ Sub___

Uranus

Makemake

Jupiter

European Lab – Columbus Orbital Facility

Earth

Sun

P6 Truss Segment

P3 Truss Segment

Pluto

Mars

Docking Compartment

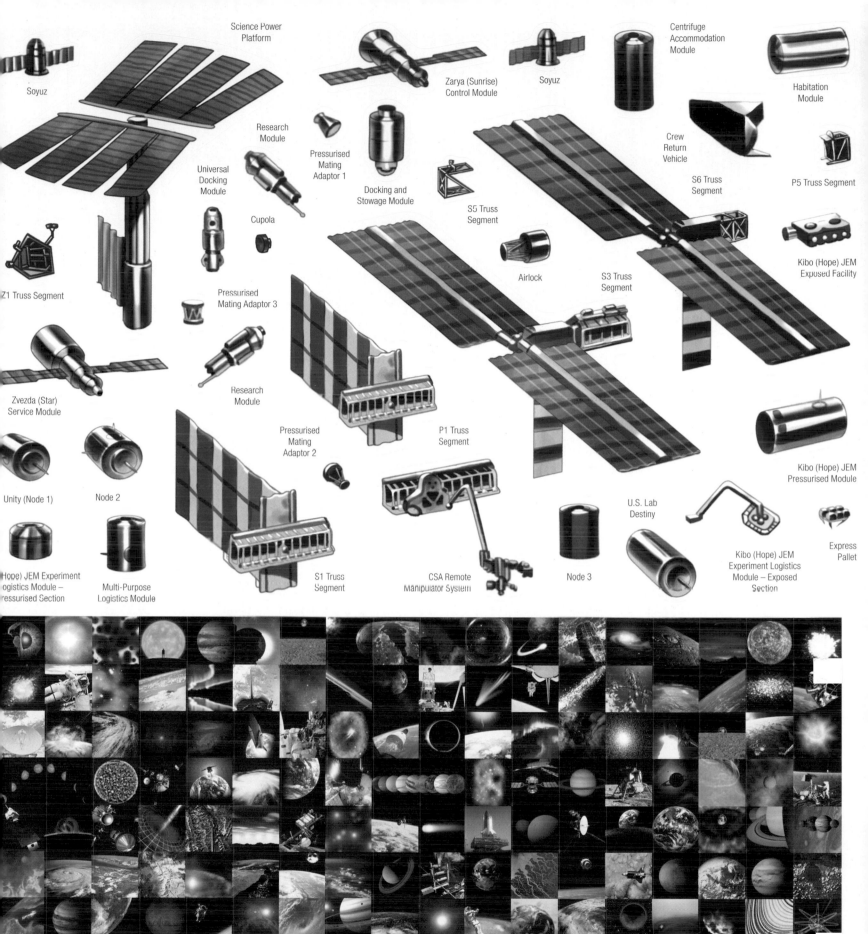

Soyuz

Science Power Platform

Zarya (Sunrise) Control Module

Soyuz

Centrifuge Accommodation Module

Habitation Module

Research Module

Universal Docking Module

Pressurised Mating Adaptor 1

Docking and Stowage Module

Crew Return Vehicle

S6 Truss Segment

P5 Truss Segment

Cupola

S5 Truss Segment

Airlock

S3 Truss Segment

Kibo (Hope) JEM Exposed Facility

Z1 Truss Segment

Pressurised Mating Adaptor 3

Zvezda (Star) Service Module

Research Module

Pressurised Mating Adaptor 2

P1 Truss Segment

Kibo (Hope) JEM Pressurised Module

Unity (Node 1)

Node 2

(Hope) JEM Experiment Logistics Module – Pressurised Section

Multi-Purpose Logistics Module

S1 Truss Segment

CSA Remote Manipulator System

Node 3

U.S. Lab Destiny

Kibo (Hope) JEM Experiment Logistics Module – Exposed Section

Express Pallet

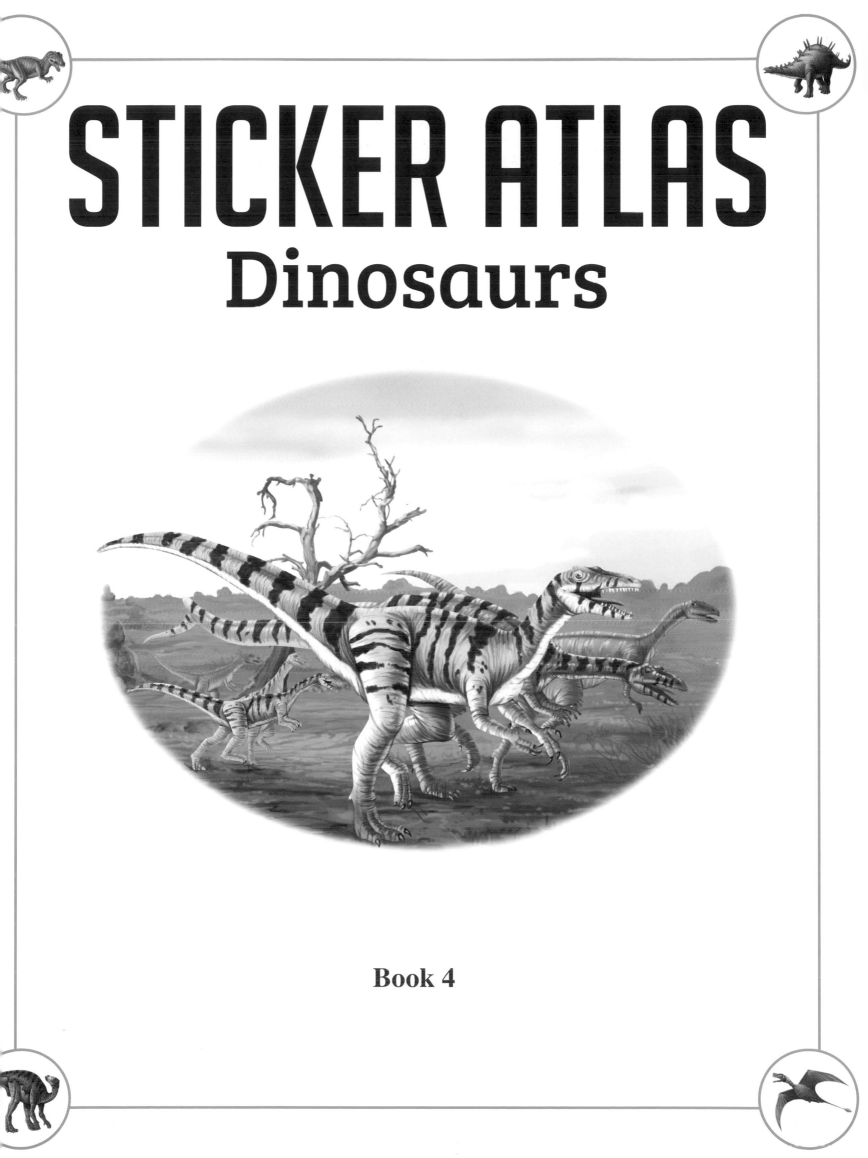

STICKER ATLAS
Dinosaurs

Book 4

Dinosaurs

Dinosaurs were powerful prehistoric animals that lived on Earth for 160 million years, before suddenly becoming extinct 65 million years ago.

Dinosaurs were scaly, egg-laying reptiles, resembling the crocodiles or lizards of today. Dinosaurs included herbivores (plant-eaters) and carnivores (meat-eaters). Some dinosaurs stood on all fours (quadrupeds), while others were bipedal, standing on their two back legs.

Everything we know about dinosaurs comes from fossil remains such as

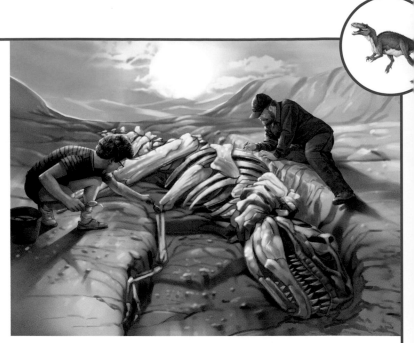

bones, teeth and claws, which were buried and turned to stone over time.

Dinosaur scales have been found, but as all fossils are stone-coloured, it is impossible to tell what colour dinosaurs were.

Dinosaur families

Dinosaurs are divided into two groups, saurischia (saw·RISK·ee·a) and ornithischia (OR·ni·THISK·ee·a). The groups are distinguished by pelvis shape. Saurischians were 'lizard-hipped', while the ornithischians were 'bird-hipped'.

The saurischian group was made up of theropods and sauropods. Theropods were fast and ferocious bipedal carnivores. They included Tyrannosaurus (ti·RAN·o·SAWR·us).

Sauropods were large, long-necked herbivores. They included Diplodocus (di·PLOD·o·kus).

The ornithischian group was made up of all the remaining dinosaurs. Some stood on two legs and some stood on four. Many of them had plates, armour, horns or spikes to protect them from predators.

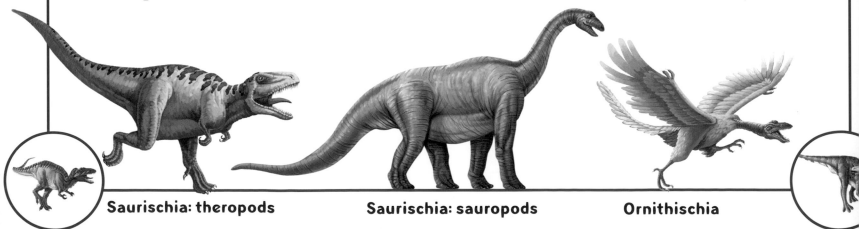

Saurischia: theropods   **Saurischia: sauropods**   **Ornithischia**

A changing earth

Since the formation of the earth, many plants and creatures have evolved and died out. Dinosaurs lived in the Triassic, Jurassic and Cretaceous periods. The first modern humans evolved less than 2 million years ago, in the Quaternary period, which we live in now.

During the time when dinosaurs ruled the world, the earth went through many changes. During the Triassic period, all the continents were joined together in one land mass we call Pangaea. The land started breaking apart and drifting during the Jurassic and Cretaceous periods, eventually dividing the earth into continents.

Triassic period

Jurassic period

Cretaceous period

The evolution of dinosaurs

The first creatures to live on Earth inhabited the ocean. They were simple organisms such as seaweed, jellyfish and shellfish. Eventually there came to be fish, land plants, insects, amphibians and reptiles.

Before the coming of the dinosaurs, Earth was inhabited by prehistoric creatures, including massive reptiles.

Unlike most reptiles, dinosaurs stood on upright legs that were located straight under their bodies. Other reptiles, including lizards, had bent legs that came out of the sides of their bodies.

Legs of a dinosaur

Modern-day lizard

Triassic period

The Triassic period extended from about 250 to 200 million years ago. The earth was not divided into continents then as it is today, but was all one supercontinent that we call Pangaea, surrounded by an ocean we call Panthalassa.

The climate of the earth at this time was hot and dry. There was hardly any life on the land during the early Triassic period, with living things mainly occupying marine environments.

Eventually, marine creatures started to inhabit the land, and it is possible that dinosaurs evolved from these prehistoric reptilians.

Some of the earliest dinosaurs appeared in the mid to late Triassic period.

They included Coelophysis (SEEL·o·FIE·sis), a slender theropod that lived in North America.

It is possible that Coelophysis lived in packs, as many fossils of this dinosaur have been found together at Ghost Ranch in New Mexico.

A flock of Coelophysis

Late Triassic dinosaurs in the European region included the large plant-eating Plateosaurus (PLAT·ee·o·SAWR·us) and Liliensternus (LIL·ee·en·SHTER·nus), a small and speedy carnivore.

Pisanosaurus (pee·SAHN·o·SAWR·us) was an ornithischian plant-eater found in South America. It was hunted by Herrerasaurus (he·RER·a·SAWR·us), a small, fast and sharp-toothed theropod.

During the late Triassic period, as the first dinosaurs were evolving on the land, pterosaurs (TER·o·sawrs), the largest flying creatures of all time, inhabited the skies. Pterosaurs were not actually dinosaurs, but massive winged reptiles.

The exact appearance of Liliensternus is unknown – it might have been covered in scales or feathers.

Scaled Liliensternus

Feathered Liliensternus

Herrerasaurus hunting Pisanosaurus

Jurassic period

The Jurassic period took place around 199 to 145 million years ago. During the early Jurassic period, Pangaea broke up into two supercontinents: Laurasia to the north and Gondwana to the south.

The climate on Earth was warm and wet, providing vegetation and allowing dinosaurs to thrive. Dinosaurs became larger and many more species evolved.

Laurasia

In Laurasia, there was an abundance of plants and many plant-eating dinosaurs, which meant that theropod predators had plenty of prey.

North America

Jurassic North America was home to many dinosaurs. Allosaurus (AL·o·SAWR·us) was a frightening theropod – a massive meat-eater reaching about 10 metres (33 feet) in height.

There were also giant sauropods such as Apatosaurus (a·PAT·o·SAWR·us), Camarasaurus (KAM·a·ra·SAWR·us) and Diplodocus (di·PLOD·o·kus), some of the biggest dinosaurs that ever existed.

It is estimated that Diplodocus reached around 50 metres (164 feet) in length.

Europe

In Europe, a 9-metre-long (30-foot) carnivore called Megalosaurus (MEG·a·lo·SAWR·us) reigned.

The late Jurassic period in Europe was also home to what scientists think was the first ever bird, Archaeopteryx (AHR·kee·OP·ter·iks).

Asia

Asia was home to Yangchuanosaurus (YAHNG·chwahn·o·SAWR·us), a horned theropod that preyed on sauropods including Mamenchisaurus (mah·MUHN·chee·SAWR·us) and Omeisaurus (UH·may·SAWR·us), as well as ornithiscian stegosaurs.

Stegosaurus

Apatosaurus

Allosaurus

Gondwana

The new supercontinent of Gondwana was warm and flourishing, with plants providing plenty of food for animals, which were growing in size and number.

South America

Gondwana was home to large sauropods like the short-necked Brachytrachelopan (BRAK·e·TRAK·o·LO·pan). South America's sauropods continued growing and evolving, and by the Cretaceous period they were among the largest creatures to have ever walked the earth.

Africa

During the Jurassic period, massive dinosaurs appeared in Africa including the frightening theropod Ceratosaurus (se·RAT·o·SAWR·us), distinguishable by its horn, its massive jaws and predatory nature.

Kentrosaurus (KEN·tro·SAWR·us) was a stegosaurian similar to North America's Stegosaurus (STEG·o·SAWR·us). It was a spiky ornithischian living in the area of Tanzania, alongside massive sauropod Brachiosaurus (BRAK·ee·o·SAWR·us). Massospondylus (ma·so·SPON·di·lus) was a smallish, bipedal sauropod found in South Africa.

Dimorphodon

Megalosaurus

Chungkingosaurus

Cretaceous period

The Cretaceous period took place around 144 to 65 million years ago. During this time, the supercontinents of Laurasia and Gondwana broke up further, into the continents we have today.

Much of the land was covered by shallow water, and chalk rocks formed across the earth. The climate became cooler and seasons began. New life appeared, such as flowering plants, and with them, bees. Cretaceous Earth was also home to some of the first mammals and insects. The dinosaurs of the Cretaceous period were diverse and huge in size.

North America

Quetzalcoatlus

Quetzalcoatlus, a flying reptile, had a wingspan of 12 metres (39 feet).

During the Cretaceous period, North America was divided into islands because of high water levels. It was full of vegetation and flowering plants, as well as tall trees. In the sky was Quetzalcoatlus (KWET·zal·ko·AT·lus), the largest being ever to fly.

North American sauropods began to die out in the Cretacean period and were replaced by horned dinosaurs and hadrosaurs – duck-billed dinosaurs.

Edmontosaurus (ed·MON·to·SAWR·us) was one of the largest hadrosaurs, measuring about 13 metres (43 feet) in length, and it cohabited with the hadrosaur Parasaurolophus (PAR·a·saw·ROL·o·fus), which had a large crest on its head.

Triceratops (trie·SER·a·tops) was a massive plant-eating ornithischian that used its frill and three sharp horns to protect itself from predators such as Deinonychus (die·NON·i·kus) and Tyrannosaurus (ti·RAN·o·SAWR·us).

Deinonychus was a small theropod that possibly hunted in packs, and used the sharp claws on its feet as powerful weapons against its prey. Tyrannosaurus was a fearsome hunter, with massive jaws and teeth that it used to tear and devour prey.

Tyrannosaurus   **Parasaurolophus**   **Edmontosaurus**

Europe

Like North America, much of Europe was covered by shallow seas, and most Cretacean dinosaurs lived on the tropical islands that remained above water.

Baryonyx (BAR·ee·ON·iks) was a large carnivore that used its sharp teeth and hooked claws for hunting marine animals.

Iguanodon (i·GWAHN·o·don) was a bulky herbivore that could stand on two legs or on four. Close relations of Iguanodon were the duck-billed hadrosaurs, including Telmatosaurus (TEL·ma·to·SAWR·us).

Baryonyx hunting fish

Dsungaripterus

A Protoceratops and Velociraptor have been found fossilised in combat. Both dinosaurs died during the fight, probably due to a collapsing sand dune.

Asia

Asia was the largest continent in the Cretaceous period and was home to many living creatures. Massive reptiles such as Dsungaripterus (JUNG·gah·RIP·ter·us) dominated the skies.

On the land was Gigantoraptor (jig·ANT·o·RAP·tor), a large theropod that resembled a huge ostrich. Saichania (sie·KAHN·ee·a) was bulky and armoured, equipped with a club-like tail. Protoceratops (PROH·to·SER·a·tops) was a horned plant-eater about the size of a sheep. Velociraptor (vee·LOHS·i·RAP·tor) was a small, fierce theropod.

Gigantoraptor   **Protoceratops**   **Saichania**   **Velociraptor**

South America

Saltasaurus (SAHL·tah·SAWR·us) and Rinconsaurus (RIN·kon·SAWR·us) were among the sauropods to inhabit Cretaceous South America. There was also Unenlagia (oon·en·LAHG·ee·a), a strange-looking theropod whose name means 'halfbird'. Giganotosaurus (jig·a·NOT·o·SAWR·us) was a giant carnivore found in Argentina.

Unenlagia

Giganotosaurus

Rinconsaurus

Saltasaurus

Africa

Massive Spinosaurus (SPIE·no·SAWR·us), which had massive spines up to 2 metres (6.5 feet) long growing out of its back, ruled Africa, along with other carnivorous dinosaurs such as the giant theropod Carcharodontosaurus (kahr·KAR·o·DON·to·SAWR·us), with its massive jaws and serrated teeth.

There was also Deltadromeus (DEL·ta·DROHM·ee·us), another theropod giant, whose slender body shape and long limbs suggest it was a very fast runner.

Carcharodontosaurus means 'shark tooth lizard'.

Carcharodontosaurus

Oceania

Minmi (MIN·mee) and Muttaburrasaurus (muht·a·BUHR·a·SAWR·us) were Australian dinosaurs found around Queensland. Muttaburrasaurus was an ornithopod and Minmi was a very small, armoured ankylosaur.

Minmi

Deltadromeus

Jobaria

Lurdusaurus

Muttaburrasaurus

Extinction

All dinosaurs suddenly became extinct 65 million years ago, along with many other living creatures. This mass extinction is known as the Cretaceous–Tertiary extinction event.

There are several theories on why dinosaurs became extinct. Some scientists believe that it was due to the rapid change in atmosphere and climate that took place during the late Cretaceous period.

Others believe that Earth was hit by an asteroid or comet, which caused extreme temperatures that led to the extinction of most life on Earth.

Some believe that dinosaurs did not change their diet as the plant life changed, and so became extinct from lack of food.

The extinction event wiped out about three-quarters of life on Earth. Among the survivors were mammals. Much smaller than dinosaurs, these warm-blooded creatures were now free of the giant predators that had ruled Earth. Other survivors included the birds that now took over the sky, as the flying pterosaurs were all gone. Animals continued to evolve and diversify and eventually the earth became as it is today.

An icy Earth

How to use your giant wall map

Dinosaur fossils have been found all over Earth, and from these fossils we can guess where and when dinosaurs lived. The wall chart shows a map of Earth, divided into the continents as they are today. On the continents are spaces for you to place the stickers of dinosaurs and other creatures that lived in those parts of the world during the Triassic, Jurassic and Cretaceous periods.

North America

Chirostenotes
(Jurassic)

Triceratops
(Cretaceous)

Deinonychus
(Cretaceous)

Alamosaurus
(Cretaceous)

Acrocanthosaurus
(Cretaceous)

Apatosaurus
(Jurassic)

Camarasaurus
(Jurassic)

Coelophysis
(Triassic)

Parasaurolophus
(Cretaceous)

Ceratosaurus
(Jurassic)

Albertosaurus
(Cretaceous)

Pteranodon
(Cretaceous)

Diplodocus
(Jurassic)

Edmontosaurus
(Cretaceous)

Hypacrosaurus
(Cretaceous)

Stegosaurus
(Jurassic)

Gargoyleosaurus
(Jurassic)

Tyrannosaurus
(Cretaceous)

Quetzalcoatlus
(Cretaceous)

Remember, the world was a changing place in the time of the dinosaurs and not all dinosaurs shared the earth at the same time. The stickers have the names of the creatures printed under them. Choose a dinosaur sticker, then look for a picture that matches that sticker on the map. Place the sticker over the picture and you're done!